First published 1964
Second impression 1966
Third impression 1970
SBN 11 290082 8

Cover: American Locomotive 1875 (see Plate 17)
Note : All the items illustrated in this booklet are part of the Science Museum collections

A Science Museum
illustrated booklet

RAILWAYS

1 : To the end of the
nineteenth century

by T. M. Simmons
M.A, A.M.I.Mech.E

Her Majesty's Stationery
Office London 1964

During the early part of the nineteenth century such great strides were made in the design and construction of railway locomotives and in the laying down of many miles of railway track, that this period is often considered as the beginning of the railways. In fact, they began much earlier. This booklet will illustrate, somewhat briefly, early railway history to the end of the nineteenth century, whilst a second publication will deal solely with railway development during the twentieth century.

The rail track can be traced back to the mines of the early sixteenth century. At this time, mined material was transported to the pit bottom on sledges and wheelbarrows. When the floor of the roadway was soft, the wheel of the barrow and the sledge runners penetrated into the ground; this difficulty was overcome by the laying of planks. The two planks on which the sledge was hauled, generally by children, was in fact the embryo rail track. The Germans replaced the sledge with a mine tub known as the 'Hundt' (dog); which had four wheels, the leading two being smaller and nearer together than those at the rear. It was also provided with a circular disc of wood projecting downwards from the base, and between the two front wheels, which ran between the two planks and thereby kept the wheels, and hence the tub, on its proper path (Agricola: *De re Metallica*, 1556).

As far as is known the first rail track to be installed in England was by Huntingdon Beaumont in 1604 at the Woollaton Colliery, near Nottingham. This track carried coal for a distance of two miles. It is also recorded that in the latter half of the sixteenth century wagons were in use at the copper mines near Keswick, but whether rails were employed is not known.

In 1608 Beaumont left Nottingham and installed rail tracks at mines in the northern coalfields. Although his system was not taken up very rapidly, by the end of the century many miles of wooden rails had been installed to transport the coal from the mines to the staithes sited on the rivers Tyne and Wear, where it was loaded into ships and brought to London or exported elsewhere. Coal from many mines was transported by this means, but where the pits were some considerable distance from the river, pack-horses with panniers were employed to carry the coal. Some collieries employed as many as 600 horses daily to transport the coal to the staithes.

This arrangement was slow and expensive, and, in time, engineers such as George Stephenson turned their attention to find a cheaper and more efficient method.

The employment of rails was not only an efficient means of transporting coal but also for moving other materials. For instance, in 1731, a merchant by the name of Ralph Allen, anxious to move more and more quarried stone from its source to the nearby Avon, built a roadway on which he laid wooden rails. The laoded wagons ran readily downhill to the unloading point, but horses were required to haul the wagons back up the incline to the quarry. A general view of this operation is illustrated in plate 1 : a typical wagon of this period used by Allen and others is shown in plate 2.

It will be seen that the wheels on this wagon are fitted with flanges ; but when flanges on wheels were first introduced is a little obscure. We know from Agricola that flanged wheels were not in use. For Agricola, had he known either of true flanged wheels, or of 'rowlers' would have made mention of them in his exhaustive work *De re Metallica*. It is known that Dr Edward Brown, F.R.S. visited the gold mines of Chemnitz in 1669, and on his return talked of tubs or chests capable of carrying four hundred pounds of spoil which ran on eight wheels. Brown is of course describing, not an eight-wheeled truck, but a truck with four wheels and four rowlers, both affixed to the axle, but running separately from each other. The rowler had a lip, not unlike the flange as we know it today, which is indeed confirmed as being in use on the wagons that ran over Ralph Allen's wagon way near Bath in 1731. It would be unwise to be dogmatic on the actual date that the flanged-wheel was introduced. It is established that it was in use by the mid-eighteenth century, and there is reliable evidence that a form of flange was being employed as early as the mid-seventeenth century. It is best left there.

With the advent of the industrial revolution there was an increasing demand for improved and more rapid methods of transportation for the finished goods as well as for the raw materials required, and for the movement of more and more coal to fire the boilers providing steam to operate the many beam engines motivating the factory machinery. Up to this time, the movement of raw materials and finished goods had been almost entirely dependent on the pack-horse.

The solution to the problem began when Newcomen designed and operated his beam engine in 1712. This can be considered to be the first successful application of steam to provide power. James Watt, Richard Trevithick and many others, were later to build improved stationary engines to provide power for the mines and factories.

Trevithick, who was connected with the tin-mining industry in Cornwall, successfully converted one of his stationary engines into a locomotive (Plate 3) to haul wagons between Merthyr Tydfil and Abercynon. Later, in 1808, he constructed the locomotive 'Catch me who can' which he operated on a circular track in London, hauling wagons on which interested persons were given a joyride. Unfortunately both locomotives were too heavy for the type of rails then in use.

It was not until the second decade of the nineteenth century that the possibilities of the steam engine for the transport of materials and later passengers came to be fully appreciated. George Stephenson, engineman at the Killingworth Colliery, developed and installed several stationary engines for use on the surface and underground. As a result of his experiments he built his first locomotive 'Blucher' in 1814. At the same time, William Hedley, Jonathan Foster and Timothy Hackworth, all mining men, were also working on locomotive designs for use at other collieries in Northumberland. 'Puffing Billy,' built a year earlier, was the result of Hedley's endeavours (Plate 5).

George Stephenson, later to become known affectionately as the 'father of railways' was a self made, self educated man (Plate 4). Despite failures, he continued to build locomotives to haul coal from the pithead to the staithes. It became apparent too that the locomotive could be adapted for passenger service, despite the considerable opposition which was displayed by the landowners and those who operated stage coach services. The merits of the locomotive over the horse were established once and for all at the Rainhill trials in 1829 when Stephenson's 'Rocket' (Plate 6) won the contests, reaching the unheard-of-speed of nearly 30 mph.

The Rocket and other locomotives later hauled passengers and freight on the Liverpool and Manchester Railway, which can be considered to have provided the first really regular passenger service. Throughout his life, George Stephenson maintained his great interest in railway matters, and after becoming a Member of Parliament lost no opportunity in driving home the fact that steam power had outmoded horse power. His great pioneering work was carried on by his son Robert.

The pioneers in Britain were soon followed and copied by engineers in Europe ; of whom Marc Seguin was perhaps one of the most well known. Seguin invented an ingenious locomotive whose tender not only carried the fuel and water, but had built into it two fans which were driven from the wheels and so, as the locomotive moved along a form of forced draught was supplied to the fire in the fire box. A fine model of this locomotive is illustrated at Plate 7. At the beginning of the railway era, when already passengers as well as freight were being carried, the passengers either travelled in open wagons, or even in or on coal chaldrons, or they arranged for their road carriages to be strapped to flat wagons. At this time, journeys by train were draughty and hazardous; in addition the smoke from the locomotive was most unpleasant. Not until several years after the opening of the Liverpool and Manchester Railway in 1830, did the first railway carriages (Plate 8) running on their own wheels, properly sprung and with recoiling buffer stops, come into use.

By 1834 the volume of traffic was rapidly increasing on the railways and it became imperative to provide increased control over the running of trains, and to ensure the safety of the passengers. Up to this time trains had been signalled through by hand, but it was now decided to introduce various forms of fixed signals along the track which would indicate the state of the line ahead; coloured lamps were used at night, white lights indicating the 'all clear' signal, but these were soon changed to the now familiar 'Green' still in use today. A white light readily became distorted, and in foggy weather, or under smoky conditions could easily be confused with the 'Red' danger signal. Plate 10 illustrates four signals in use up to about 1856, when the first experiments with the interlocking of signals and points were introduced.

The style of station architecture was extremely ornate in the nineteenth century, and examples of this can be seen at such stations as York and Shrewsbury. Euston, until its recent demolition in 1963, probably was the finest example of this extravagant style in London. A new design of station made its appearance with the opening of the Metropolitan Railway, which had to make use of deep shafts to allow a degree of natural daylight to penetrate to the subterranean depths. Examples of this type of design may still be seen today at Edgware Road, Mansion House and Baker Street (Plate 12).

The importance of the role which the railways played in the industrial revolution of Great Britain is illustrated by the fact that from their inception to the end of the nineteenth century, 19,000 miles of railway track were laid and in use, over which were transported raw materials, manufactured goods, and passengers. By 1900, 500,000 miles of track were in use throughout the world.

About 1860, a new form of public passenger conveyance was considered, namely the tramcar. The pioneer of this form of transport was G. F. Train, who introduced it from America. It was of course originally horse-drawn, but later was operated by steam; it being quite easy to convert the horse-drawn vehicle into a trailer for attachment behind the steam prime mover. (Plates 15 and 16.) By the end of the nineteenth century there were very few towns of importance which did not possess a public tramway system. The electric tramcar made its appearance in England in 1885, the first system being installed at Blackpool.

1 Prior Park 1731

This print has been selected as the first in this series, since it is now regarded as possible the earliest pictorial evidence of the use of rails for the conveyance of heavy objects.

At this time, stone for building purposes was in ever-increasing demand. Mr Ralph Allen, the owner of Prior Park, near Bath, conceived the idea of using a railway to run his wooden trucks from the local quarries to barges moored in the nearby river Avon. The wagon way had wooden rails and ran the full length of Mr Allen's property; its roadway was made sufficiently wide to permit use by pedestrians and other traffic, in addition to the quarry wagons.

The coloured engraving shows the single track of wooden rails on which are two loaded trucks running down towards the river, each with a brakesman to control it. It also illustrates the style of dress of the period, and the magnificence of the homes of wealthy landowners.

2 Eighteenth century timber railway and quarry truck

About the time that Ralph Allen was building his wagon way in Somerset other merchants were doing the same in the Forest of Dean on the other side of the Bristol Channel, in order to move not only timber and stone but also the coal which was being mined in this area.

The illustration depicts a model of a wagon introduced by Ralph Allen for the movement of stone from his quarries near Bath.

The truck was carried on four cast-iron wheels having deep flanges to prevent it from leaving the rails. One wheel on each axle was fixed, the other being free to rotate independently. The loaded trucks descended by gravity and were controlled by a brakesman walking behind them, who was able to retard all four wheels separately. The return journey was usually made by two horses hauling the empty wagons up the hill, the brake levers having been removed and placed inside the wagon. The sides of the wagons were also removable.

The maximum carrying load is said to have been about four tons, and early records show that the cost of building these wagons was about £30.

3 Richard Trevithick's Locomotive 1804

This interesting model was built to illustrate how the first steam engine to run on rails was constructed. For several years before Trevithick's experiment, steam engines had been used in a stationary role, replacing hand-operated and horse-driven engines. The model is largely conjectural, for no records exist to show exactly how the original locomotive was built. It appears to have been based on the Llewellyn tram engine drawing of December 1803, being fitted with rail wheels to suit the guauge of the Pen-y-darran line.

The general design of the engine is very similar to that of Trevithick's single cylinder high-pressure engine used for driving machinery; and an interesting comparison can be made by first observing the stationary engine which is on exhibition in the Motive Power collection, and then studying this model. It can then be seen how ingeniously Trevithick adapted the stationary design to that of a locomotive. The piston and cylinder position is altered from a vertical to a horizontal one.

The Pen-y-darran engine, as it is often referred to, made its first run on 11th February, 1804, undertaking several journeys between Merthyr Tydfil and Abercynon. It weighed 5 tons and was capable of hauling a load four times its own weight at a steady 5 mph. However, it proved too heavy for the rail track, which being made of cast iron was frequently fractured.

4 Oil Painting of the Stephenson Family

This picture has been included as it is of interest both as a family group and because it shows in the background an early type of locomotive then being introduced for colliery work, to replace the horse for the conveyance of coal from the pits to the staithes.

This genre painting shows six figures; the men are George Stephenson, his son Robert and possibly George Stephenson's father. An engraving of this picture (or of the original if this is a copy) was published in 1862 and gives Lucas as the artist and the title as 'The Birthplace of the Locomotive; Killingworth Colliery and George Stephenson's Cottage'.

The locomotive in the background is generally typical of the period when George Stephenson was chief engineman at the Killingworth Colliery (1809-1812), but the smokebox is shown in a position which was in fact not adopted until 1830.

5 The Locomotive 'Puffing Billy' 1813

The great importance of this locomotive, and the reason for its inclusion in this collection of railway masterpieces, is that with its sister locomotive 'Wylam Dilly' (on exhibition in the Royal Scottish Museum, Edinburgh), it is the earliest surviving full-size locomotive in the world.

As far as can be ascertained from surviving records, Puffing Billy was built at Wylam Colliery by William Hedley, who had as his assistants Jonothan Foster and Timothy Hackworth. The locomotive was used over a five mile stretch of track between Wylam and the staithes at Lemington-on-Tyne.

The Science Museum acquired Puffing Billy in 1862, after nearly fifty years' continuous service. It is of particular interest to note that in 1815, owing to the weakness of the plate way, it was rebuilt as an eight-wheeler to spread the load, but was altered back to a four-wheeler about 1830 when the line was relaid with cast-iron edge rails of a type now seen beneath it.

When the locomotive was first introduced, the noise and smoke emitted from the chimney caused such annoyance in the surrounding countryside that legal opinion was taken as to whether the owners could be restrained in some way. Satisfaction to all parties was achieved by passing the exhaust steam into a quieting chamber before discharging it into the chimney.

6 The Rocket 1829

No account, whether short or long, technical or otherwise, if it covers the first half of the nineteenth century and is concerned with the development of the railways, is complete without reference being made to the world famous locomotive 'Rocket' built by George and Robert Stephenson.

The original Rocket, or at least a substantial part of it, has been on exhibition in the Science Museum for over 100 years.

The most notable item missing is the tender, and it is only when one pauses to study the replica, so faithfully put together for the Museum by Messrs. Robert Stephenson and Company from original drawings and data, that the changes in the position of the cylinders and valve gear become apparent.

The Rocket is famous because, by winning the Rainhill Trials, it established once and for all the superiority of the steam locomotive over the horse as a means of railway haulage. The Rainhill Trials were staged as a competition to determine the most efficient locomotive for this purpose. The rules for the competition and the prize money being offered are set out in poster form, and an original may be seen in the Rail Transport collection.

7 Seguin's Locomotive 1829

At about the same time as George Stephenson was making history with the building of the 'Rocket' and the winning of the Rainhill Trials, Marc Seguin, a French engineer, was constructing the first locomotive to be built in France, for use on the St Etienne-Lyons Railway. This locomotive, a model of which is illustrated on the page opposite, is remarkable as the first locomotive in the world to be fitted with a multi-tubular boiler. Copying the practice of so many of the English engineers, Marc Seguin first tried out his engine and the capabilities of his boiler by employing it in a stationary capacity to drive machinery.

The tender is of particular interest, for not only was it built in the form of a shed-like structure to keep both driver and fuel dry, but it was also fitted with two impeller fans connected directly to the wheel axles. As the train proceeded on its journey the fans created a draught which, by means of leather flexible pipes, could be transmitted to the ash pit, and so fan the fires, thereby increasing the steaming and thermal efficiency of the locomotive.

8 First Class carriage of the Liverpool and Manchester Railway 1834

Until this date, all wagons on railway trains were of the open type and intended only for the carriage of merchandise. In 1825, at the opening ceremony of the Stockton and Darlington line a new departure was made in that a covered-in wagon was included in the special train for the use of the Directors of the Company.

Not until after the opening of the Liverpool and Manchester railway in 1830 did railway carriages specially fitted for the conveyance of passengers come into regular use.

The model railway carriage shown therefore demonstrates a definite advance in style. For until its introduction, if passengers were carried, they either travelled standing up or squatting in open wagons, or travelled in their road coaches which were mounted on to flat wagons which could be coupled to the end of the railway train.

The body of this properly-designed railway carriage was divided into three compartments having doors at each side and each holding six passengers, three a side. The upholstery was well padded, and arm rests were provided. Each compartment also had six windows, in the doors and beside each corner seat. The windows in the doors were provided with sliding panels to permit the top half to be lowered. The centre of the roof of each compartment was fitted with an oil lamp to provide illumination. Because of the poor light provided, it became the practice of passengers to carry their own candle lamps for reading purposes; examples of these lamps can be seen in the Rail Transport collection.

9 The Norris Locomotive 1843

In the introduction to this booklet it was stressed that the pioneers of railway design and of locomotive construction were the British, but by the middle of the nineteenth century other countries in Europe were developing their own designs, often as a result of acquiring the Stephenson-built locomotive and later modifying it to suit their own particular requirements.

The illustration depicts a model of a locomotive designed by an American engineer William Norris, a Philadelphian, which has a special four-wheeled swivelling bogie for use on lines having steep inclines and sharp curves. It was found to be particularly suited also to the terrain in Austria and as a result the Austrian railways acquired one of Norris's locomotives and named it 'Austria'.

Interesting features of this locomotive were the design of the tender, and the manner in which the water tank fitted in horseshoe form around the inside wall, leaving an almost oval space for the fuel.

Locomotives at this period were becoming larger in size and heavier in design. This locomotive and tender weighed 14 tons whilst the Rocket was but half of this weight.

Left.   The earliest form of fixed signal for day use was introduced on the Liverpool and Manchester Railway in 1834. It consisted of a red flag stretched across a frame which, by means of a lever, could be turned to face the driver to show danger. When set parallel to the rails it indicated all clear. Red and white lights fixed to a post served the same purpose at night.

Left centre.   This type of signal was introduced on the Great Western Railway in about 1837. It consisted of a wooden post with a bracket and pulleys at the top and, by means of a cord, a ball was drawn to the top to indicate 'Safety' or lowered to the ground to indicate 'Danger'. At night a stable lantern was used instead of the ball.

Right centre.   One of the earliest signals introduced on the London and South Western Railway, in about 1840, was of this form. The disc was rotated by a cord fastened to its edge and passed round guide pulleys. The signal was intended to control two lines of traffic; if the closed part of the disc was turned to the left it indicated the left line was occupied, and similarly when turned to the right that the right road was blocked. If the aperture was to the top then both lines were blocked. For night use, two lamps on separate spindles, located either side of the main post, indicated the position by showing red for danger, and green for all clear.

Right.   This signal was in the form of two circular discs mounted on a horizontal shaft. The shaft was counterweighted so that the discs were normally vertical, indicating danger. If they were pulled horizontal it indicated all clear.

All the signals described here were operated by men on the side of the rail pulling cords or turning handles. Prior to the introduction of these types of signals trains were signalled through by railway employees waving flags—red for danger and white for 'all clear'.

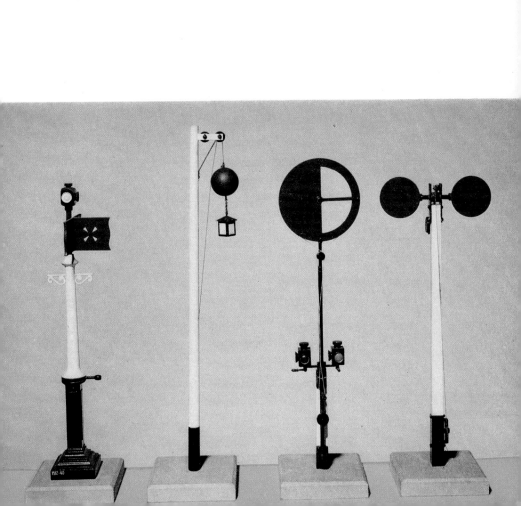

11 Broad Gauge Locomotive of the Firefly Class 1840-42

This contemporary model is of a standard broad gauge locomotive named 'Ixion', which was designed by Daniel Gooch, and was built for the Great Western Railway by Messrs Fenton, Murray and Jackson in October 1841. The locomotive was largely based on the design of the 'North Star' built by Robert Stephenson and Co. in 1837, which had proved so successful on the Great Western Railway.

Ixion earned much fame as the locomotive selected to represent the supporters of the Broad Gauge in the Gauge Commission's trials of 1845; and despite the fact that subsequently the protagonists of the Standard Gauge (4ft 8½in) won the day, the Directors of the Great Western Railway continued to operate broad gauge locomotives and rolling stock until 1892.

The track on which the model stands is a perfect scale reproduction of the 7ft Broad Gauge.

12 A Standard Locomotive of 1845

Built a little later than the Gooch type of locomotive, this type of standard locomotive was in general use on the ever-increasing railway systems which were being opened all over the country as the result of what Robert Stephenson called the 'Railway Mania'.

The smoke box was completely enclosed and supported the cylinders, the valve chests were above the cylinders, and the valves were driven through a rocking shaft by four eccentrics and the ordinary link motion. A dome over the firebox carried a spring-loaded lever safety valve whilst another dome on the boiler barrel accommodated the regulator which was of the rotary butterfly type.

This particular model has been included in the booklet because it shows the general trend of design. It is beginning to resemble the familiar locomotive of the early twentieth century, without, of course, the power that the later locomotives were able to develop.

13 Tank Locomotive of the Dublin and Kingstown Railway 1851

This locomotive was one of the later types to be built by the Company in their locomotive works in Dublin, for the first Irish Railway which had opened in 1834 with a length of track of six miles. It was renamed 'Alexandra' in 1865, after it had been employed in pulling the train used by the Prince and Princess of Wales on their official visit to Dublin.

At the rear of the footplate was a tank, sufficiently large to hold enough water for one journey; it was flanked by two coal bunkers. A spectacle plate was also provided behind the top of the firebox to protect the driver and his assistant from the elements. The complete engine was constructed on one rigid frame, and the general appearance of the locomotive, which weighed over 20 tons, began to show marked similarity to the remaining tank engines still in use today. Prior to 1841 most of the locomotives were built by Messrs G. Forrester and Co. of Liverpool.

14 Baker Street Station 1863

This view of Baker Street Station as it was just over one hundred years ago is still recognisable in parts of the station today, particularly at the platforms used by the Inner Circle line, where the inclined openings formed through the side walls and leading up to the street above, which used to admit daylight to the station, although now blocked up are still visible.

The coloured lithograph shows clearly the style of dress of the period, and also demonstrates how the variation in gauge of the rails was overcome. The track is laid in such a way that either broad gauge or standard gauge traffic could use the line. However, within a year of opening, the Metropolitan Railway had gone over completely to standard gauge track.

London Transport have familiarised the public with this scene of the early days on the Metropolitan Railway by using it as a poster to announce the Centenary Celebrations in 1963 organised by the London Transport Executive.

15 Steam Tramcar of 1872

The tramcar played an important part in the transportation of the public by rail during the latter half of the nineteenth and the first quarter of the twentieth century.

Practically every city or town of any size had its own tramway system which, at a time when there were few motor cars and buses, was the principal means of transporting the general public. Cars, buses and trolley-buses have now replaced the tram, and the only tramway system in England at the present time is at Blackpool. On the continent of Europe trams of the single-deck type hauling a trailer are still very common.

The model is of a steam-driven tramcar patented by Mr J. Grantham in 1871, which was used on the tramway operating between Victoria Station and Vauxhall. It shows an additional feature patented by Mr Grantham in that it is designed to run on the road or on rails whichever is desired. There are four flangeless wheels near the ends which carry the tram on the road. One pair are the driving wheels and the other pair, which run loose on the axle are mounted on a swivel carriage for steering. For use on rails, two axles are fitted with smaller wheels placed nearer to the centre, one wheel of each pair being flanged. These could be lowered by levers until they bore on the rails. The drive, however, was through the flangeless pair of larger wheels which ran on the road outside the track rails.

16 Double Deck Tramcar trailer 1879

On the Continent the tramcar is still extensively used, and it is common practice to attach trailer cars to the prime mover for the carriage of merchandise, or for the carriage of additional passengers.

In Great Britain, where the use of the tramcar is now practically extinct, the use of the trailer was seldom employed. This may have been due to lack of space in the urban areas through which the trams ran; or because, unlike most Continental countries, Britain did not use trams for inter-urban journeys, routeing them through the countryside along their own paths quite separately from the normal highway. Distances did not justify such a course; also the railway systems of the country were completely adequate.

The illustration shows a model of a typical trailer tramcar of the latter part of the nineteenth century for town use, which has been adapted for attachment to a steam driven tramcar as prime mover; originally it had been designed to be drawn behind a horse.

17 American Locomotive 1875

Early locomotives to be constructed for use on the railways of the United States of America were either direct orders from British firms, or adaptations from British protypes. But the model illustrated is of typical American design, with outside cylinders and four coupled driving wheels, and with a four-wheeled leading bogie out front. The framing which is of the bar type, is almost universally adopted in America; where its greater flexibility is considered to reduce the strains due to irregularities of the permanent way. The locomotive has outside cylinders with the valve chest above; the valves receiving their motion from a weigh-shaft driven by the usual link motion from inside eccentrics on the driving axle. There is a long stroke feed-pump driven from one crosshead, and a large injector is also provided. The tender is carried on two four-wheeled bogies, and the engine is provided with a large enclosed cab for the protection of the driver and stoker during the severe weather. Owing to the unprotected state of the railway and the frequency of level crossings, a strong cow-catcher is attached to the buffer beam, and a large bell and head-lamp are carried on the boiler to give pedestrians some warning of the approach of a train.

This model of one of the celebrated class with single driving wheels 8 ft in diameter was designed by Patrick Stirling. It proved to be so successful that it worked the express traffic of the Great Northern Railway for nearly thirty years. The first of the class, known as 'Stirling No 1', was built in 1870, and this full-size locomotive is now preserved by the British Railways Board. The locomotive represented by this model was built at the Doncaster Works in 1887. It differs but slightly from the original No 1. The locomotive and its tender (not illustrated) weighed $78\frac{1}{2}$ tons, and had a working steam pressure of 170lb/sq in. A vacuum cylinder beneath the footplate applied the brakes to the driving and trailing wheels. It is of interest to note that the leading bogie is pivoted behind the centre, there being no transverse motion.

This locomotive was built almost exactly 50 years after George Stephenson's 'Rocket'; and it will be seen that in design, weight and steam pressure great improvements had been made.

19 Compound Locomotive 1885

The model shows one of Francis Webb's three-cylinder compound engines of the 'Dreadnought' class, built for the London and North Western Railway. This type of engine was a great step forward in locomotive construction. The distinctive feature of the Webb compound engine was that the steam from the boiler first entered a pair of outside high-pressure cylinders driving the trailing axle, while the exhaust from both of these passed into one low-pressure inside cylinder driving a separate axle. This gave a reduced temperature range within the cylinders, and also the advantage of four driving wheels without employing coupling rods. When starting, the engine could work non-compounded, the exhaust from the high-pressure cylinders passing directly to the blast-pipe; while reduced boiler steam was supplied to the low-pressure cylinder.

The tender carried only 1,800 gals of water, and 5 tons of coal, because it was fitted with a scoop for picking up water whilst travelling at speed. The scoop was designed by John Ramsbottom in 1860.

The model is of a locomotive, designed by Mr W. Adams for the London and South Western Railway in 1890, and built at the Company's Nine Elms Works.

This class of locomotive was still in use some fifty years later and must therefore be familiar to many readers today. Starting life on the express trains from Waterloo to either Bournemouth or Exeter, it was finally relegated to hauling local traffic between Southampton, Bournemouth, and Weymouth, and between Southampton, Salisbury and Templecombe.

The locomotive had a working steam pressure of 175 lb/sq in, and was fitted with Howe's link motion which gave a cut off varying from 75 per cent with full gear on starting to 17 per cent in the normal running condition. A notable feature was Adam's specially designed blast pipe fashioned in the form of a vortex.

Science Museum illustrated booklets

Cameras Photographs and Accessories

Agriculture Hand tools to Mechanization

Fire Engines and other fire-fighting appliances

Astronomy Globes, Orreries and other Models

Surveying Instruments and Methods

Physics for Princes The George III Collection

Motor Cars Up to 1930

Steamships: Merchant ships to 1880

Warships: 1845-1945

Published by
Her Majesty's Stationery Office
and obtainable from the
Government Bookshops listed
on cover page iv (post orders
to PO Box 569, London SE1)

7s each (by post 7s 4d)

Printed in England for
Her Majesty's Stationery Office
by W. Heffer & Sons Ltd
Cambridge

Dd. 501662   K.160